The Wondrous Wizard of ID

Brant Parker and Johnny Hart

CORONET BOOKS
Hodder Fawcett Ltd., London

Copyright © 1965, 1966 by Publishers
Newspaper Syndicate
Copyright © 1970 by Fawcett Publications Inc.
First Published 1970 by Fawcett Publications
Inc., New York
Coronet edition 1972
Second impression 1972
Third impression 1973

Printed and bound in Great Britain for
Coronet Books,
Hodder Fawcett Ltd,
St. Paul's House, Warwick Lane,
London, EC4P 4AH
by Hazell Watson & Viney Ltd,
Aylesbury, Bucks

ISBN 0 340 15818 2

SO MUCH FOR MANEUVERS.

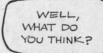

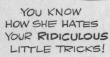

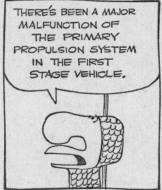

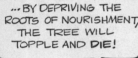

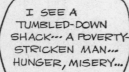